THE

# DAILY SPARK

***180 easy-to-use lessons and class activities!***

## THE DAILY SPARK

Critical Thinking
Critical Writing
Great Books
Journal Writing
Math Word Problems
Poetry
Pre-Algebra
SAT English
Shakespeare
Spanish
Spelling & Grammar
U.S. History
Vocabulary
Writing

SPARK PUBLISHING

Spark Publishing
A Division of Barnes & Noble Publishing
120 Fifth Avenue
New York, NY 10011
www.sparknotes.com

ISBN-13: 978-1-4114-9980-5
ISBN-10: 1-4114-9988-8

Please submit changes or report errors to www.sparknotes.com/errors.

Printed and bound in Canada.

Written by Rebecca Ortman.

# Introduction

The *Daily Spark* series gives teachers an easy way to transform downtime into productive time. Each of the 180 exercises—one for every day of the school year—will take students five to ten minutes to complete and can be used at the beginning of class, in the few moments before turning to a new subject, or at the end of class. A full answer key in the back of the book provides a detailed explanation of each problem.

The exercises in this book may be photocopied and handed out to the class, projected as a transparency, or even read aloud. In addition to class time use, they can be assigned as homework exercises or extra-credit problems.

Use the *Daily Spark* to help your students master the basics of Spanish, including pronunciation, grammar, vocabulary, and cognates. Each exercise in the *Spanish Daily Spark* gives students practice with all kinds of beginning-level topics using fun, funny prompts. ¡*Ole*!

Spark your students' interest with the *Spanish Daily Spark*!

# Animal, Vegetable, or Mineral?

You've probably heard about Hispanic singers "crossing over" to the English world. Singers like Ricky Martin, Enrique Iglesias, and Gloria Estefan all started their careers by singing in Spanish. At some point these bilingual stars decided to expand their fan base by singing in English, too. **Crossover words** are Spanish words that have entered the English language, and vice versa.

Take five minutes to list as many Spanish crossover words as you can think of in English. Use the following categories:

| Animals | Foods | Music | Expressions |
| --- | --- | --- | --- |
| llama | | | |

# Cogn@tes

Spanish is a Romance language: it comes from Latin, the language of the Romans. Because of the great influence of Latin on the English language, there are also many words in Spanish that resemble English words. These are called **cognates**.

Take a look at cecili@89's online profile. How much of it can you translate? Look for cognates and crossover words.

> ¡Hola! Soy cecili@89.... Mis amigos me llaman "la Ceci." Soy una persona inteligente y seria—pero soy también muy sociable. Tengo muchos amigos. Mi verdadera pasión es el arte—todos me dicen que soy super creativa. ¡Me fascina pintar! Un día seré famosa. ¿Quieres charlar conmigo? Dále....

# You Can't Always Trust Your Friends

If your friend is smiling, she or he is probably happy. If a Spanish word looks like an English word, it probably means the same thing. Unless it doesn't. Some words (and friends) are wolves in sheep's clothing. Words that look similar but have different meanings are called **false friends**.

Fill in the English sentences with the correct Spanish words. Then check your answers. Use a dictionary if you need to.

1. The books at our school __________ are in terrible shape. One would expect teenagers to respect communal property.
2. I don't like wearing jeans. Call me a wimp, but the __________ is just too rough for my skin.
3. You'll have to use a lot of __________ to get that ketchup off your shirt. Start scrubbing!
4. Can you please __________ *The OC* episode for me? I have to finish this term paper.
5. Theo's mother yelled at him for spilling grape juice on the white __________. Then she hid the spot under a rug.

# What's Your Sign?

Take a look at the horoscope below. Write down all the cognates you recognize. Then look up the words to make sure they're not false friends.

Tauro: Los asuntos de tus financias requieren de tu inmediata atención. Las cosas están estables por ahora, pero un tornado está por venir. Prepárate.

# What's in a Name?

Here's a puzzle for you. Olivia Lane arrives in the airport of a Spanish-speaking country. Her Spanish is pretty shaky, so when the immigration officer asks her for her name, she somehow becomes Olivia "Leni." How did it happen?

Here's the answer: she spelled out her last name in *English*, not in Spanish (*l-a-n-e* instead of **ele-ah-ene-eh**).

Depending on how complicated your name is, you may find yourself in the same situation as Olivia. You have to learn how to say the letters of the alphabet in *Spanish*.

Work with a partner. Take turns spelling out your whole names in Spanish: first, middle, and last.

# E-ESE-PE-ELE-ELE O-U-TE

Work with a partner. One person reads the Spanish letters, and the other writes down what he or she hears. Then switch. What words do the letters spell?

a-b-u-rr-i-d-o

g-u-a-p-o

c-l-a-s-e / d-e / e-s-p-a-ñ-o-l

a-l-m-u-e-r-z-o

# Call All of It as You See It

Unlike English, Spanish is a phonetic language. In other words, each letter of the alphabet has its own distinct sound (or sounds, in the case of *c*, *g*, and *s*). Each time you see that letter, you can be certain that it will be pronounced in the same manner. But first, forget your English pronunciation!

Work with a partner. One person reads the sentence out loud, and the other corrects the pronunciation.

El General Zapato observa a la señora cortar la piña en la calle. ¡Qué hambre tiene! (*General Zapato observes the lady cutting the pineapple on the street. How hungry he is!*)

# Your Jokes Stress Me Out!

In Spanish, if you don't see an accent mark on a word, you stress either the last or second-to-last syllable. If you do see an accent mark, however, you stress the accented vowel.

Work with a partner. Read the two jokes below out loud to each other. Pay attention to how your partner stresses the words.

**Había una vez un hombre tan pequeño que se subió encima de una canica y dijo, "¡El mundo es mío!"** (*There was once a man so small that he climbed on top of a marble and said, "The world is mine!"*)

**Había una vez un señor tan perezoso que soñó que estaba trabajando y amaneció cansado.** (*There was once a man so lazy that he dreamt he was working and woke up tired.*)

# Hello Nice to Meet You Good-bye!

How many ways can you greet someone in Spanish? How many ways can you say "good-bye"? Take five minutes to fill in the chart with as many expressions as you can.

| Hello | Good-bye |
| --- | --- |
| | |

# Salutations

Imagine you're participating in a summer program in Costa Rica. Read each of the following situations. Then choose the most appropriate expression: **hasta mañana, buenos días, hola, chau,** or **buenas tardes.**

- It's 9:30 A.M., and you're down in the kitchen, getting a glass of juice. Your host grandmother, a very proper Costa Rican woman, walks in. You say, "__________, **señora.**"
- After a long day of sightseeing in San José, you're ready to go to sleep. You get up from the couch and say to your host family, "__________."
- Your host brother, Andrés, is on his way to his summer job at the bank. You, luckily, aren't going with him. As he leaves, you say, "¡__________, **Andrés!**"
- On your way home from class, you run into a cute classmate. You call out, "¡__________!"
- You're tired of walking in the afternoon heat. You hail a cab. When you get in, you say, "__________, **señor.**"

# Such Drama

Be the director and create a role-play for Molly and Theo. Follow the cues in English.

**Molly:** [Say hi to Theo. Then introduce yourself.]

______________________________________________

**Theo:** [Tell Molly it's nice to meet her.]

______________________________________________

**Molly:** [Ask Theo what his name is.]

______________________________________________

**Theo:** [Tell Molly your name is Theo.]

______________________________________________

# Respectfully Yours

Which title of respect is most appropriate for each of the following people? Think carefully about your relationships with these people and how each person would expect to be addressed.

Your Spanish teacher

a. **Señorita**

b. **Profesora**

A clerk at your local **bodega** (*corner store*)

a. **Señor**

b. **Licenciado**

A young woman you meet on the subway or bus

a. **Señora**

b. **Señorita**

An elderly family friend

a. **Doña**

b. **Señorita**

# Piccionario

Work with a partner. One of you should draw a classroom object, and the other one should say what it is in Spanish. Don't worry if your artistic skills are lousy—this is Spanish class, not art class.

Choose from the following words: **el pupitre, el libro, la mesa, la pizarra, el lápiz, la pluma.**

# Señor Subject and Señora Predicate

In Spanish, as in English, a sentence is formed by combining a subject and a verb or predicate. The **subject** is the person or thing that you're talking about, generally a noun. The **predicate** is everything else.

Complete the sentences with words you know. Use the cues.

____________ (choose a subject) se llama Señor Slimy. Señor Slimy ____________ (choose a predicate).

____________ (choose a subject) es la novia (*girlfriend*) de Señor Slimy. Todos los días, Señor Slimy y su novia ____________ (choose a predicate). ¡Cuidado (*careful*), amigos!

# So Eloquently Scrambled

In English, our sentences usually follow the format **subject + verb**. But in Spanish, the subject can come either before or after the verb. This flexible word order makes for a very eloquent language.

Unscramble the following sentences, listing all of the possibilities.

asquerosa (*disgusting*) / la cafetería / en / la comida / es

su novio / del equipo de fútbol / el capitán / es

fría / me gusta / la pizza

# From January to December and Back

Name the months in order, in Spanish. Don't write them down. Now name them backward, starting with December. How'd you do?

# Countdown

Answer the following questions with a number word in Spanish (for example, **seis** or **veintiuno**).

How many students are in your Spanish class? ______________________

How many classes have you already had today? ______________________

How many times has your mind drifted in class? ______________________

How many minutes before the bell rings? ______________________

How many days before your next vacation? ______________________

# I Like Turnips, but I Hate Yams!

To say you like something, use the following expressions:

- **Me gusta + [what you like, singular].**
- **Me gustan + [what you like, plural].**

To say you don't like something, use the following expressions:

- **No me gusta + [what you don't like, singluar].**
- **No me gustan + [what you don't like, plural].**

Write two sentences about which vegetables you like and two sentences about which vegetables you detest.

# 50 Cent or Clay Aiken?

To ask if someone likes something, use the following expressions:

- **¿Te gusta + [thing or idea]?**
- **¿Te gustan + [things or ideas]?**

Work with a partner. Find out which bands or singers your partner likes by asking **¿Te gusta...?** questions.

# My Grandmother's Pet Rabbit, Sir Shedzalot

On a separate sheet of paper, draw your family tree. Label each person with his or her name and relationship to you in Spanish (for example, **Tía Betty, Abuela Matilda,** etc.). Include all of the family pets that you remember (for example, **Tortuga Slopoke**).

# Time to Tell Time

To tell the time in Spanish, say:

- **Es la + [time (for one o'clock)].**
- **Son las + [time (for all other hours)].**

Instead of A.M., Spanish speakers say **de la mañana**. For P.M., they say **de la tarde** or **de la noche**. Take a look at a time-zone map of the United States. Then complete the sentences, using the following model:

- **Cuando son las tres de la mañana en California, <u>son las seis de la mañana</u> en Nueva York.** (*When it's three A.M. in California, it's six A.M. in New York.*)
- **Cuando son las cinco de la mañana en Pennsylvania, ________________ en Colorado.**
- **Cuando son las cuatro de la tarde en Florida, ________________ en Texas.**
- **Cuando es la una de la mañana en Nuevo Mexico, ________________ en Utah.**
- **Cuando son las ocho de la noche en Hawai'i, ________________ en Alaska.**
- **Cuando son las dos de la tarde en Oregon, ________________ en Vermont.**

If you have access to a computer, here's the URL for an online time-zone map: http://www.timetemperature.com/tzus/time_zone.shtml.

# Some Days Are Better Than Others

Answer the following questions in Spanish. You don't have to write complete sentences. Remember that the days of the week in Spanish aren't capitalized.

Which is your favorite day of the week? ____________________

On what day is your hardest class? ____________________

What day of the week feels like it never ends? ____________________

What day of the week is loaded with boring classes? ____________________

On what day of the week do you hang out with friends? ____________________

On what day of the week does your mom or dad nag you the most? ____________________

# Tick Tock

Draw clocks representing the following times. (Draw traditional clock faces, not digital ones.)

las cinco menos diez

las doce y media

la una y quince

las tres en punto

las siete y cuarto

# No Excuses

Match the classes to the descriptions. You should get them all right the first time—they're all cognates. No excuses!

| | | |
|---|---|---|
| ____ | 1. This is where you refuse to shower in the locker rooms. | a. historia |
| ____ | 2. This is where your lab partner faints when she has to dissect the frog. | b. matemáticas |
| ____ | 3. This is where you forget how to do long division. | c. arte |
| ____ | 4. This is where you accidentally spill paint all over your classmate. | d. biología |
| ____ | 5. This is where you're forced to memorize useless dates, like 1503. | e. educación física |

# An A+ in *Química*

Complete the columns with your class names in Spanish.

| Classes You're Failing | Classes You're Acing | Classes You're Just Passing |
| --- | --- | --- |
| | | |

# You Want Me to Do What?

At some point you're going to have to recognize Spanish instruction lines. You can start by following this one: **Traduzcan las siguentes instrucciones.**

¿Cierto o falso? ______________________________

Contesta las preguntas. ______________________________

Entrevista a tu compañero. ______________________________

Trabajen en grupos. ______________________________

Completa las oraciones. ______________________________

# So Do You Love Me or Not?

You may have already noticed that Spanish and English have slightly different ways of punctuating questions and sentences. Add Spanish punctuation marks to the following dialogues. Their meanings will change depending on how you punctuate them.

**Julieta:** Me amas Romeo
**Romeo:** No puedo vivir sin ti

**Señor Tengomucho:** Tienes un dólar
**Señor Nolatengo:** No tengo veinticinco centavos

**Fulanito:** Quieres ir a la discoteca
**Fulanita:** No me parece mala idea

**Mamá:** No estás feliz jaimito
**Jaimito:** No estoy feliz

# Oops, Wrong Number

When people give their phone numbers in Spanish, they often say them (and write them) in groups of two. If the number has an uneven number of digits, as we have in the United States, the last number will remain by itself. For example, the number 721-8348 would be written as 72-18-34-8 and said, verbally, as **setenta y dos, dieciocho, treinta y cuatro, ocho.**

Write down the phone numbers of five friends or family members. Then write out how you would say them.

# The Rain in Spain Stays Mainly in the Plain

Spanish vowels are never silent. They should be pronounced clearly, distinctly, and always in the same way. Each a in mañana, for example, has the same sound. They don't vary like the *o*'s in the English word *tomorrow.*

Work with a partner. Take turns reading the following proverbs aloud. Note that we've included the colloquial English equivalents, rather than the direct translation, for each Spanish proverb. Pay attention to how your partner pronounces the vowels.

Ver es creer. (*Seeing is believing.*)
Del dicho al hecho hay un gran trecho. (*Easier said than done.*)
A diario una manzana es cosa sana. (*An apple a day keeps the doctor away.*)
Cada loco con su tema. (*To each his own.*)

# Planes, Trains, and Automobiles

How do you get around town? By bus? By subway? By bicycle? Answer the following questions. Use the construction Voy + en (or a, in the case of a pie) + [means of transportation].

How do you get to school every day? ______________________________

How do you get to the mall? ______________________________

How do you get to your best friend's house? ______________________________

How do you get to the park? ______________________________

How do you get to the movies? ______________________________

# Getting Personal

We often use names to tell who is doing an action. We also use **pronombres personales**, or subject pronouns. Fill in the chart with the subject pronouns.

| Person | Singular | Plural |
| --- | --- | --- |
| 1st | | Feminine:<br>Masculine: |
| 2nd | Informal:<br>Formal: | |
| 3rd | Feminine:<br>Masculine: | Feminine:<br>Masculine: |

# Formally Speaking

Imagine you're traveling in Nicaragua or another Spanish-speaking country. How would you address the people you meet? Unlike English, Spanish differentiates forms of address as informal or formal. Deciding when to use which form can sometimes be challenging for non-native speakers.

Look at the list of people you might encounter while traveling in Nicaragua. With whom do you use tú, and with whom do you use usted? Sort the people into two columns.

- Your classmate
- A hotel clerk
- Your dad
- The bus driver
- A five-year-old child
- A museum guard

# A Master of Pronouns

Before learning verb tenses, you should first master the subject pronouns. Complete the equations below with the correct subject pronouns. Remember, **la práctica hace al maestro** (*practice makes perfect*).

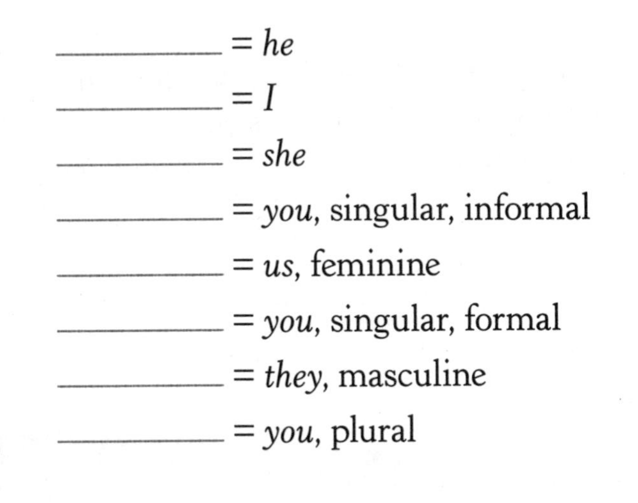

_____________ = *he*

_____________ = *I*

_____________ = *she*

_____________ = *you*, singular, informal

_____________ = *us*, feminine

_____________ = *you*, singular, formal

_____________ = *they*, masculine

_____________ = *you*, plural

# To *Ser* or Not to *Ser*

You've probably already used the verb **ser** (*to be*) to talk about yourself and where you come from. **Ser** is one of the most important verbs you'll learn, because it's used so frequently. **Ser** is irregular, which means that its forms don't follow a regular pattern.

Test your memorization skills. Spend twenty seconds looking at the present-tense forms of **ser** (in your textbook). Then write down as many forms as you can remember, with their corresponding subject pronouns.

# A Mnemonic *Service*

The verb **ser** has several uses. How many can you think of? Write down at least three, and then come up with a mnemonic device or acronym for remembering them.

# What's It Like to Be Famous?

You're a reporter with *US Weekly* and have been assigned to write a story about a famous celebrity. What would your readers want to know about the hottest star of the moment? Make a list of questions you might ask using the verbs **ser, estar,** and **gustar.**

# Desperately Seeking Fido

Oh no! Your lovable family pet has run away, looking for greener pastures or more wet food. You decide to post "Lost Pet" signs around the neighborhood, in the hopes that someone will return him or her.

Create a sign. Try to use some form of the verb **ser** at least twice. Include your pet's name, your name, and your phone number. You might start with **Busco a mi mascota** (*I'm looking for my pet*)....

# Chatterbug9 from NYC

Write your online profile for Spanish-speaking people to read. Include your screen name and your location. Tell your new friends which activities you like and dislike using the following constructions: **me gusta + [infinitive]** and **no me gusta + [infinitive]**. Write at least four sentences.

# Canto Como Un Gato Moribundo

Conduct a survey among your friends. Ask them the following questions. Compile their answers and write a summary of your findings in Spanish.

¿Estudias todas las noches?

¿Dibujas bien?

¿Cantas bien?

¿Escuchas música rap?

¿Hablas mucho en clase?

# Confident Conjugation

Are you confident in your conjugation abilities? Test yourself by filling in the blanks with the correct conjugations.

Third-person plural of llegar: ______________________

First-person singular of viajar: ______________________

Second-person singular of hablar: ______________________

First-person plural of escuchar: ______________________

Second-person plural of dibujar: ______________________

Third-person singular of comprar: ______________________

# *Bailar*, with a Twist

Conjugate the present tense of the verb **bailar,** but add a twist. Start with the third-person plural and work your way backward to the first-person singular.

# An Intruder Within

In Spanish, nouns have a gender: they are either **masculine** or **feminine**. Sort the following words into one of two columns: masculine or feminine. But be careful! Some are intruders that may trick you.

cuaderno
mano
miel
mesa
poema
libro
profesora
león
foto
sabor

# The More the Merrier

In Spanish, as in English, nouns are distinguished as being **singular** or **plural**. Take a look at the following pairs of the same noun. Fill in the blank with the correct form. Watch your spelling.

una mano, dos ___________

un ___________, dos lápices

una problema, dos ___________

una ___________, dos nacionalidades

un país, dos ___________

una ___________, dos palabras

# Articles for a Party

In Spanish, feminine nouns are usually accompanied by definite articles. Definite articles are equivalent to the English word *the* and point out something specific. In Spanish, use:

- **El** with singular masculine nouns
- **La** with singular feminine nouns
- **Los** with plural masculine nouns
- **Las** with plural feminine nouns

Imagine you're organizing a surprise birthday party for your friend. Write a list of items you need. Be sure you include the correct definite articles.

# Rules Are Made to Be Broken

You may have learned several rules for determining the gender of Spanish nouns. Here's a sad realization: there are so many exceptions to these rules, you may begin to wonder why rules were made in the first place.

Take a look at the following words. First label them as masculine or feminine. Then write down the rule that each is breaking.

día
radio
sal
planeta
moto
piel

# Researching an Article

In Spanish, as in English, nouns can be accompanied by **indefinite articles**. Indefinite articles are equivalent to the English *a* and *an*, and they specify one (un or una) or several (unos or unas) items or objects, without giving an exact number.

You've got a paper due for history class, so you head to the library to do some research and get some sources. Tell the librarian what you need by filling in the blanks below with the correct indefinite articles.

Necesito _____ libros sobre (*about*) la Segunda Guerra Mundial (*World War II*).

Necesito _____ revista (*magazine*) americana de junio de 1941.

Necesito _____ artículo del periódico (*newspaper*) inglés durante (*during*) la Guerra.

Necesito _____ fotos de Alemania en los años 1940s.

# That's Definitely It

Which article—the definite or indefinite—would you use in each of the following situations?

You're in chemistry, and you forgot to get a thermometer for your experiment. You tell your teacher: Necesito ____ termómetro, por favor.

You see some funky blue pants in a store window, and you fall in love with them. You tell the salesperson: Quiero ____ pantalones azules.

Your little brother takes the last apple, which you were about to eat. You tell him: ¡Dame ____ manzana!

You decide to have fries with your lunch. You go up to the cafeteria cook and say: ____ papas fritas, por favor.

# Spanish Does He Speak?

In Spanish, there are several ways of turning a statement into a question. The resulting questions may sound like Yoda-speak to you, but they'll make sense to Spanish-speakers.

Turn the following statement into three questions that ask the same thing:

**Max habla español.**

# The Five+ Ws

As in English, Spanish questions begin with question words. Write down all of the English question words that come to mind. (Hint: there are more than the five Ws.) Then try to fill in the second column with the Spanish equivalents.

| English Question Words | Spanish Question Words |
|---|---|
| | |

# The Third Degree

Pay attention to verb forms when answering questions. The verb form in the answer will be based on the one in the question. If the question is asked of **tú**, for example, the answer should be in the **yo** form. If the question is about **ustedes**, the answer should be in the **nosotros** form.

Answer the following questions using the correct verb form.

¿Cuándo conversa Ana con sus amigas? ____________________

¿Cuándo descansas, Manuel? ____________________

¿Cuándo regresamos a la escuela? ____________________

¿Cuándo estudian ustedes el español? ____________________

# Yes, I'm a Regular Card Shark

First, turn the following statements into yes / no questions. Then survey your classmates. Try to find at least one classmate who does each of the following activities.

jugar al póquer (*play poker*)

acampar en las montañas (*camp in the mountains*)

montar a caballo (*ride horses*)

bucear en el mar (*scuba dive in the sea*)

# Guess Who?

Which seasons match the descriptions? Complete the sentences with the correct Spanish seasons. Don't forget to include the definite articles.

I'm the worst season ever, because when I come around, it's school time again. No more swimming pools and trips to the beach! **Yo soy** ________________.

Ah-choo! I make you sneeze up a storm, because along with me comes lots of pollen. But my new flowers are so beautiful that you can forgive me … right? **Yo soy** ________________.

I make the city asphalt so hot that it melts the soles of your flip-flops. Turn on the AC! **Yo soy** ________________.

Brrrrrr! You'd better bundle up, or I'll chill you to the bone with my ferociously cold winds. And tomorrow I'll send a nor'easter your way. **Yo soy** ________________.

# Conjugation Abomination

Write down ten **-er** verbs. Then, for fun, conjugate all of their present tense plural forms.

# Serve It Up

Imagine you can have anything you want to eat ... no parents nagging you about which foods are good for you, and no internal voices telling you that what you crave is too fattening or greasy or sweet. Write six sentences in Spanish about what you decide to eat and drink for breakfast, lunch, and dinner. Use the correct forms of comer and beber.

# Check Your Brainwaves

How much of an intellectual are you? Fill out the following survey to find out. Each sí answer gives you one point. You get no points for no answers. At the end, add up your points.

- A score of 1 or 2 means that you're low on the intellectual factor.
- A score of 3 means you're a closet intellectual.
- A score of 4 or 5 means you should get out more.

| | Sí | No | Puntos |
|---|---|---|---|
| 1. ¿Lees el periódico todos los días? | | | |
| 2. ¿Comprendes más de (*more than*) dos idiomas? | | | |
| 3. ¿Asistes clases avanzadas (*advanced*)? | | | |
| 4. ¿Escribes cartas (*letters*) al presidente? | | | |
| 5. ¿Recibes notas (*grades*) perfectas? | | | |
| | | Total | |

# A Verbal Discussion

Time yourself: without looking at your book, fill in the chart with the present-tense forms of **discutir** (*to discuss*). How long did it take you? **Discute** your time with the person sitting next to you.

<table>
<tr><th>Person</th><th>Singular</th><th>Plural</th></tr>
<tr><td>1st</td><td>yo:</td><td>nosotros / as:</td></tr>
<tr><td>2nd</td><td>tú:</td><td rowspan="2">ustedes:<br><br>ellos:<br><br>ellas:</td></tr>
<tr><td>3rd</td><td>usted:<br><br>él:<br><br>ella:</td></tr>
</table>

# I'm Partying on Saturday and Sleeping on Sunday

What are your plans for the weekend? Complete the schedule below. Use ir + a.

El viernes de noche ______________________________.

El sábado de mañana ______________________________.

El sábado de noche ______________________________.

El domingo ______________________________.

# Off to the Circus

Use ir + a to make sentences out of the following words. Don't forget to conjugate properly.

Julia y Mari / centro comercial (*mall*)

tú / partido de fútbol (*soccer match*)

nosotros / escuela

yo / circo (*circus*)

ustedes / restaurante

# I'll Take Fishing over School Any Day

Write a travel brochure for a summer camp for teenagers. What kinds of activities will the teenagers do? Use the correct conjugations of ir + a + [infinitive]. Write at least four sentences.

Here's some vocabulary:

ir de pesca (*go fishing*)
jugar voleibol (*play volleyball*)
montar en bicicleta (*ride the bicycle*)
pasear en bote (*take a boat ride*)
hacer una barbacoa (*have a barbeque*)

# Find Me a Head of Lettuce and a Dance Floor

You've been selected to participate in a new reality show in which contestants hunt down common and uncommon items. Where would you go to find the following objects? Write down the places and their definite articles in Spanish.

a pair of blue jeans: ____________________

a bar graph: ____________________

a soccer ball: ____________________

an encyclopedia: ____________________

a head of lettuce: ____________________

# What a Bummer!

Which expression would you use in each of the following situations?

Your friend Suzie tells you a great bit of gossip.
You say:

a. ¡No me digas!
b. ¡Genial!

After much cajoling, your parents allow you to go to the Battle of the Bands competition. You say:

a. ¡Qué chévere!
b. ¡Qué lástima!

Your friend gulps down a super-sized soda in under ten seconds. You're pretty grossed out. You say:

a. ¡Genial!
b. ¡Vaya!

Pete's in trouble. His parents are grounding him for two weeks. You say to him:

a. ¡Qué bien!
b. ¡Qué pena!

# Looking for Harmony

In Spanish, as in English, the verb in the predicate of a sentence should agree in person and in number with its subject. This is called **subject-verb agreement**. You wouldn't say, "I is from Boston," so don't do it in Spanish, either.

Take a look at the following sentences. Some of them display subject-verb agreement, and some of them don't. Correct the ones that don't so that they make grammatical sense.

Teodoro nunca comen vegetales.
Yo soy de San Antonio, Texas.
Ustedes tomamos jugo de naranja en la mañana.
La clase de historia es muy aburrida.

# Are You Going to the Beach, or Are We Going to the Park?

Unscramble the following sentences. Think carefully about subject-verb agreement while you put together the sentences.

yo / estudias arte / y / estudio matemáticas / tú

es profesora / y / son estudiantes / la mujer / los niños

nosotros / y / ustedes / van a las montañas / vamos a la playa

# *Una Manzana* a Day Keeps *La Doctora* Away

What foods do you eat todos los días? What foods do you eat a veces (*sometimes*)? What foods do you eat nunca (*never*)? Fill in each column with at least three foods.

| Todos Los Días | A Veces | Nunca |
| --- | --- | --- |
| | | |

# And for the Entree, We Have....

Imagine you're cooking dinner for your family. You'll need to go to the supermarket and pick up the ingredients. Write a shopping list in Spanish of food items you'll need for your meal.

Here's some vocabulary:

**un poco de** (*a little*)
**unos / as** (*some*)
**una libra de** (*a pound of*)
**un kilo de** (*a kilogram of*)

# Change It Up

**Stem-changing verbs** don't follow the normal pattern of regular verbs. The stressed vowel of the stem changes when the verb is conjugated.

Conjugate the following o ⟶ ue verbs. Follow the prompts. Include the subject pronouns.

volver, first-person plural: ____________________

dormir, second-person plural: ____________________

poder, third-person singular: ____________________

encontrar, third-person plural: ____________________

# To Get the A, You've Got to Study Every Day

Complete the paragraph with the correct form of the verb in parentheses. Don't forget your e ⟶ ie verbs.

Daniela ________ (*cerrar*) el libro de química, y ________ (*comenzar*) a llorar. ¡No ________ (*entender*)! dice. ¡No ________ (*quiero*) perder el año!

# Take Two

Fill in the chart with the present-tense forms of **repetir** (*to repeat*). When you're done, repeat the assignment on a separate sheet of paper, without looking at your first chart.

<table>
<tr><th>Person</th><th>Singular</th><th>Plural</th></tr>
<tr><td>1st</td><td>yo:</td><td>nosotros / as:</td></tr>
<tr><td>2nd</td><td>tú:</td><td rowspan="2">ustedes:<br><br>ellos:<br><br>ellas:</td></tr>
<tr><td>3rd</td><td>usted:<br><br>él:<br><br>ella:</td></tr>
</table>

# Don't Be So Possessive!

**Possessive adjectives**, like descriptive adjectives, describe people, places, and things. They express ownership or possession.

Match the following phrases to their Spanish translations.

| | |
|---|---|
| ________ 1. my pencil | a. sus discos |
| ________ 2. my pencils | b. tus cuadernos |
| ________ 3. his discs | c. sus cuadernos |
| ________ 4. her disc | d. mis lápices |
| ________ 5. your notebooks | e. su disco |
| ________ 6. their notebooks | f. mi lápiz |

# Their Names Are Jack and Jill

Answer the following questions in Spanish. Use possessive adjectives in your answers—and make sure you answer in complete sentences.

¿Cómo se llama tu madre? ______________________________

¿Cuál es la música favorita de tu mejor amigo? ______________________________

¿Cuál es tu postre favorito? ______________________________

¿Cuáles son los nombres de tus primos? ______________________________

# The School Bathrooms Are Biohazardous

In both English and Spanish, **adjectives** describe people, places, and things. Think about the following places. Which Spanish adjectives could you use to describe them? Use at least two words per item.

la cocina de un restaurante de comida rápida (*fast food*)

tu sitio preferido (*your favorite hangout*)

la habitación de tu hermano menor (*younger*)

la oficina de un cirujano (*surgeon*)

el baño de tu escuela

# Frisky Is ... Frisky

Adjectives are often used with the verb ser to point out characteristics of nouns, such as color, size, appearance, and so on.

Write a sentence to describe each of your family members. Don't forget to include your pets. Use at least one adjective per sentence, as well as the correct conjugation of ser.

# Your Boyfriend's Hot!

In English, the forms of descriptive adjectives do not change to reflect gender and number. In Spanish, however, they do. If you're talking about a girl, for example, you have to use a feminine, singular adjective. Choose the adjective that completes the sentences below.

Mi tío Larry es ________.
a. bajo y gorda
b. bajos y gordos
c. bajo y gordo

Los gemelos (*twins*) son ________.
a. rubias
b. rubios
c. rubio

¡La señora Ortiz es muy ________!
a. antipática
b. antipático
c. antipáticas

¡Qué ________ es tu novio!
a. guapa
b. guapos
c. guapo

# Opposites Attract

Match each adjective to its opposite.

| | |
|---|---|
| ______ 1. bonito | a. pequeño |
| ______ 2. simpático | b. delgado |
| ______ 3. alto | c. viejo |
| ______ 4. gordo | d. feo |
| ______ 5. joven | e. antipático |
| ______ 6. grande | f. bajo |

# Adjective, Jr.

Some descriptive adjectives have both long and short versions, depending on where they fall in the sentence.

Circle the word that completes each sentence.

Emilia es una (*buena / buen / bueno*) amiga.

Mi profesor de historia es muy (*mala / mal / malo*).

Nelson Mandela es un (*gran / grande*) hombre.

*Don Quijote* es un (*buena / buen / bueno*) libro.

¡María, tu familia es tan (*gran / grande*)!

Hoy es un (*mala / mal / malo*) día.

# Did You Just Call Me Old and Fat?

The meanings of some adjectives depend on where they are placed in relation to the corresponding nouns (whether before or after). Be careful with these special adjectives, because misuse can result in offense. And you wouldn't want to offend someone, right?

What do the following sentences mean? Write their translations in the spaces provided. Think carefully about the placement of the adjectives.

Mi profesora es una **gran** mujer. ______________________________

Mi profesora es una mujer **grande**. ______________________________

Jorge es un **viejo** amigo. ______________________________

Jorge es un amigo **viejo**. ______________________________

El **pobre** niño está perdido (*lost*). ______________________________

El niño **pobre** está perdido. ______________________________

# Problem Solved!

In Spanish, several verbs have yo forms that are irregular in the present tense. The rest of their forms are regular.

Read the following problems. What can you do to solve them? Complete the sentences by using the correct yo form of the verbs hacer, poner, salir, and traer.

**Problema**: Me siento perezoso. (*I feel lazy.*)
**Solución**: Yo ______________ a correr.

**Problema**: Tienes hambre. (*You're hungry.*)
**Solución**: Yo te ______________ una manzana.

**Problema**: Tengo mucho sueño. (*I'm very sleepy.*)
**Solución**: Yo ______________ un café.

**Problema**: Hace frío. (*It's cold.*)
**Solución**: Yo me ______________ un suéter.

# Charades

In groups of three, play a game of charades. Each person should think of two phrases containing the verbs **hacer, poner, oír, traer,** and **ver.** The first person to guess correctly acts out the next charade.

# It's Still Sunny in Miami

In English, the verb *to be* is used to describe weather conditions. Spanish, however, uses the verb **hacer** (*to make*).

What's your weather forecast for each of the following cities? Write complete sentences using the verb **hacer.**

Houston, Texas, in August: ______________________________

San Francisco, California, in October: ______________________________

New York, New York, in January: ______________________________

Miami, Florida, any time of the year: ______________________________

# I'm Only Happy When It Rains

Choose three kinds of weather. What do you like to do in each one? Write six sentences that start with **Cuando hace + [weather], me gusta …**

# How'd the Home Team Do?

Write out basketball scores in Spanish.

Florida 100, Florida State 82

Stanford 78, UCLA 77

Princeton 67, Harvard 56

Kentucky 98, Tennessee 74

Vanderbilt 88, Virginia 85

Purdue 91, Indiana 75

# I Know That Verb Well

Fill in the chart with the present-tense forms of conocer (*to know*). How well do you know this verb?

<table>
<tr><th>Person</th><th>Singular</th><th>Plural</th></tr>
<tr><td>1st</td><td>yo:</td><td>nosotros / as:</td></tr>
<tr><td>2nd</td><td>tú:</td><td rowspan="2">ustedes:<br>ellos:<br>ellas:</td></tr>
<tr><td>3rd</td><td>usted:<br>él:<br>ella:</td></tr>
</table>

# “Parece” Que Vas a Perder

Work with a partner. One partner asks for the conjugation, and the other one answers within ten seconds. Each correct answer is worth one point. Then, switch roles and do it again. Who got more points?

Third-person plural of **parecer**

First-person singular of **conducir**

Second-person singular of **ofrecer**

First-person singular of **traducir**

Second-person plural of **conocer**

First-person singular of **parecer**

# So I Drive a Borrowed Car

Match the questions with the corresponding responses. Then fill in the blanks with the first-person singular form of the verb in parentheses.

| | |
|---|---|
| _____ 1. ¿Tiene sed (*is thirsty*) la señora? | a. Claro, yo lo _____ (*traducir*). |
| _____ 2. ¿Tienes un carro, Julie? | b. No lo _____ (*conocer*). |
| _____ 3. ¿Quién es el muchacho? | c. Sí. Le _____ (*ofrecer*) una vaso de agua. |
| _____ 4. El libro está en francés. ¿Me ayudas a leerlo? (*Will you help me read it?*) | d. No, _____ (*conducir*) el carro de mis padres. |

# Does It Count if He's a Cartoon Character?

**Adjectives of nationality** are formed like other descriptive adjectives. Unlike in English, they are not capitalized.

Where are the following celebrities from? Use an adjective of nationality to describe each one. Use complete sentences. For example, **Él es francés.**

Mischa Barton: ______________________________

Giorgio Armani: ______________________________

Salma Hayek: ______________________________

Yao Ming: ______________________________

Apu from *The Simpsons*: ______________________________

# More Than I Can Count

To say *there is* and *there are* in Spanish, use the word hay. Answer the following questions using hay. Use complete sentences. For example,
Hay veinte libros en la clase.

How many girls are in your Spanish class? ______________________

How many dollars are in your wallet? ______________________

How many TVs are in your home? ______________________

How many DVDs are in your collection? ______________________

# There's a Lot of Dirty Laundry

What's in your room? Write six sentences using hay. Make sure that:

- You use indefinite articles as necessary
- The indefinite articles agree in number / gender with the corresponding nouns
- The number words agree with the corresponding nouns

# *B*eing Irregular

Although the verb estar (*to be*) ends in -ar, it doesn't follow the pattern of regular -ar verbs. Conjugate the present tense of the verb estar. Start with the first-person forms, then conjugate the second-person forms, and end by conjugating the third-person forms.

# Another to Be

The verb estar has several uses. How many can you think of? Write down at least two. Then write complete sentences that illustrate the uses.

# He's on My Right, and I'm on His Left

Take a look around. Now answer the following questions about who's in your class. Use complete sentences.

¿Quién está a tu derecha? ______________________________

¿Y quién está a la derecha de él / ella? ______________________________

¿Quién está a tu izquierda? ______________________________

¿Y quién está a la izquierda de él / ella ______________________________

# Upstairs and Around the Corner

Think about your school. Where are the following rooms, in relation to one another? Write six sentences in Spanish about where they are located. For example, **La biblioteca está cerca de la cafetería** (*The library is close to the cafeteria*). Use the following phrases: **al lado de, detrás de, enfrente de, a la izquierda de, a la derecha de, cerca de,** and **lejos de.**

- the library
- the gym
- the chemistry labs
- the cafeteria
- the student lockers
- the auditorium

# Where Do You Watch TV?

How well do you know the rooms of the house in Spanish? Choose the correct phrase to complete the sentence.

Cocinamos la comida en ________.
a. la sala de estar
b. la cocina
c. la oficina

Dormimos en ________.
a. los dormitorios
b. el garaje
c. el baño

Tenemos árboles y hierba en ________.
a. la cocina
b. la sala de estar
c. el jardín

Miramos la televisión en ________.
a. la cocina
b. el sótano
c. la sala de estar

# Over Here We Have the Indoor Pool

Draw a floor plan of your house or apartment. Label all of the rooms in Spanish. Don't worry about getting it perfect; just try to get the proportions right. Draw separate floor plans for each floor.

# Possessive Adjectives, Sr.

Spanish has two kinds of **possessive adjectives**—the unstressed (short) ones and the stressed (long) ones. The long ones are used for emphasis and are equivalent to the English *of mine, of yours, of his,* and so on.

Turn the short possessive adjectives into long ones and the long possessive adjectives into short ones. It won't be a simple switch: you'll have to change the order of the words.

su computadora ______________________________

las llaves mías ______________________________

tu cámara ______________________________

el carro nuestro ______________________________

mi televisión ______________________________

la casa nuestra ______________________________

# Not Interchangeable

You know that **ser** and **estar** both mean *to be*. However, they are not interchangeable.

Which of the following sentences use **estar**? Which use **ser**? Match the sentences to the correct verbs.

| | |
|---|---|
| ______ 1. Mi mamá ______ doctora. | a. son |
| ______ 2. Yo ______ muy enferma. | b. es |
| ______ 3. Mis primos ______ de Cincinnati. | c. está |
| ______ 4. La computadora ______ en el escritorio. | d. estoy |

# Oops, I Meant to Say....

Some adjectives change meaning when used with **ser** and **estar.** Take a look at the following pairs of sentences. Explain the difference between each pair of sentences.

El chico **es** listo. / El chico **está** listo.

Carolina **es** aburrida. / Carolina **está** aburrida.

El gato **es** muy vivo. / El gato **está** vivo.

La manzana **es** verde. / La manzana **está** verde.

# Right Now, Johnny Depp Is....

Write a paragraph describing your favorite celebrity. Use **ser** and **estar** correctly, and include the following:

- Where he or she is from, if you know
- What you think he or she is like
- What you think he or she is doing right now

# The Falls Are Incredible

Name five places or landmarks. Then describe each place in two sentences. Write one sentence using **ser** and one sentence using **estar**. For example, **Las cataratas de Niágara están en Nueva York. Son increíbles.** (*Niagra Falls are in New York. They are incredible.*)

# The Soccer Player Plays Soccer on the Soccer Field

Fill in the columns with words related to sports. Follow the examples.

| Deportes | Personas | Lugares |
|---|---|---|
| fútbol | ciclista | cancha |

# I Play Basketball on Sundays

Interview your classmates to find out how they like to spend their free time. Then write a summary of who does what. Ask the following questions:

- ¿Qué haces durante tu tiempo libre?
- ¿Haces deportes? ¿Cuáles?
- ¿Vas al gimnasio? ¿Cuándo?
- ¿Te gusta patinar en línea (*in-line skate*)? ¿Con quién lo haces?

# Sabes How to Conjugate Verbs?

Fill in the chart below with the present tense forms of saber (*to know*). Don't forget that it has an irregular yo form.

<table>
<tr><th>Person</th><th>Singular</th><th>Plural</th></tr>
<tr><td>1st</td><td>yo:</td><td>nosotros / as:</td></tr>
<tr><td>2nd</td><td>tú:</td><td rowspan="2">ustedes:<br>ellos:<br>ellas:</td></tr>
<tr><td>3rd</td><td>usted:<br>él:<br>ella:</td></tr>
</table>

# I'll Take the Photos if You Make the Cookies

Imagine you're the president of the Spanish club. You want to throw a party for its members, but you need some volunteers to help you with the details. Interview two classmates. Ask them if they know how to do the following activities. As you interview them, put checks in the columns.

| ¿Quién sabe...? | Yo | Compañero 1 | Compañero 2 |
| --- | --- | --- | --- |
| tocar (*play*) la guitarra | | | |
| sacar (*take*) fotos | | | |
| cantar | | | |
| hacer galletas (*cookies*) | | | |
| hacer invitaciones | | | |

# I Know, I Don't Know

Using **saber,** write a list of four activities you can do and four activities you can't do. Use complete sentences such as, **Sé jugar al ajedrez** (*chess*).

# You Know Where I Live, but I Know Karate

Fill in the blank with the correct form of saber (*to know*).

¡Cuidado! ¡El niño no ____________ nadar!

Nosotros ____________ hablar italiano.

¡Tú nunca (*never*) ____________ la hora!

Ustedes ____________ dónde vivo.

Yo ____________ kárate.

# I Think I Know the Answer....

**Saber** and **conocer** both mean *to know*. Figuring out when to use which verb can be tricky, but using the correct form is an important part of communicating in Spanish. Give some examples of when you would use **saber** and when you would use **conocer.**

# Choose Your Subject

Write four sentences using **saber** and **conocer**. Pick a word from each column. Make sure you conjugate and add **a**, if need be. For example, **Tú no conoces a mi mejor amigo.** (*You don't know my best friend.*)

| | | |
|---|---|---|
| Jennifer López<br>Paris Hilton<br>Will Smith<br>yo<br>tú<br>nosotros<br>la profesora<br>mi mamá | (no) sabe<br>(no) conoce | actuar<br>cantar<br>mis compañeros de clase<br>bailar<br>el Lago Michigan<br>mi mejor amigo (*best friend*)<br>cocinar<br>mi canción favorita |

# Can You Speak Three Languages?

You might be aware that you need to use a form of the verb *to know* to fill in the blanks below, but should you use conocer or saber? Choose the correct verb.

¿__________ dónde puedo comprar un diccionario bilingüe?
a. Conoces
b. Sabes

¿Quieres __________ a mi hermana, Javi?
a. conocer
b. saber

Soy nuevo aquí.
No __________ a nadie (*no one*).
a. sé
b. conozco

Mi amigo Ilján __________ hablar tres idiomas.
a. sabe
b. conoce

# Take *Tomar* and *Llevar*

**Ser** and **estar** both mean *to be* in English, but they have different meanings in Spanish. So do **saber** and **conocer.** There are even more verb pairs that exhibit this confusing phenomenon. Take, for example, **tomar** and **llevar.** Both mean *to take.*

Write two sentences that use **tomar** correctly and two that use **llevar** correctly.

# You Be the Teacher

Imagine you're a Spanish teacher. How would you explain the difference between **tomar** and **llevar** to your students? Give as clear an explanation as you can.

# Talking about Taking

Take the infinitive *to take*. When talking about taking, should you use **tomar** or **llevar**? Fill in the blank with the correct verb. Don't forget to conjugate!

Nosotros ____________ el autobús a la escuela todos los días.

Yo ____________ mi saxofón a clase de banda.

¿Tienes sed? ¿Quieres ____________ un vaso de cola?

Marta tiene que ____________ a su gato al veterinario.

¿Francisco, ____________ clases de francés también?

Los estudiantes ____________ sus calculadoras al exámen.

# Where's the Bathroom?

Lots of verbs in Spanish have one translation in English but several translations in Spanish. Another tricky pair is **pedir** and **preguntar,** which both mean *to ask*.

Translate the following English sentences to Spanish. Make sure you use **pedir** and **preguntar** correctly.

Matthew asks what time it is.

___

I'm sleepy. I ask for a cup of coffee.

___

My brother has no money! He asks me for five dollars.

___

My friend asks where the bathroom is.

___

# I Play, You Play

Pick a word from each column below and write four sentences that use **jugar** and **tocar** correctly. Don't forget to properly conjugate the verbs. For example, **Tú no juegas al golf.** (*You don't play golf.*)

| | | |
|---|---|---|
| Jason Kidd | (no) jugar | la guitarra |
| Eric Clapton | (no) tocar | al béisbol |
| Elton John | | la flauta (*flute*) |
| Tiger Woods | | al baloncesto |
| Derek Jeter | | el piano |
| yo | | al golf |
| tú | | la batería (*percussion*) |
| mis amigos | | al fútbol |

# I Know Where to Wear My Clothes

Classify the following articles of clothing into two columns: clothes you wear on the top half of your body, and clothes you wear on the bottom half of your body.

- la falda
- la camiseta
- la chaqueta
- los pantalones
- los calcetines
- la sudadera

# Wearing Red Again?

Take a look around the classroom. Who's wearing what color? Write four sentences about the colors your classmates are wearing. Use this model: **Julia lleva una camisa roja.** Remember that colors, in this sense, are adjectives. They must agree in number and in gender with the nouns they describe.

# It's a Dark Shade of Azure

Working alone or with a partner, answer the following questions in Spanish. Use complete sentences.

¿De qué colores es la bandera (*flag*) de los Estados Unidos? ____________

¿De qué color es la madera (*wood*)? ____________

¿De qué colores es una margarita (*daisy*)? ____________

¿De qué color es el mar (*sea*)? ____________

# How the Past Passed

The past tense in Spanish is called the **preterite**. Verb endings always tell you who does an action, but they also tell you when an action was done (in the past, present, or future).

Imagine you're at the mall with a group of friends. You split up to do your shopping, and now everyone is meeting up at the food court. What did you buy? Using the preterite tense, make sentences with the words below.

Max / un póster de The Strokes
Yo / una colonia (*cologne*) de Armani
Mis hermanos / unos discos compactos
Tú / un juego de computadora
Tú y Bianca / unas blusas de última moda (*latest style*)

# Come Play with Me!

Verbs ending in -car, -gar, and -zar have spelling changes in the yo form in the preterite tense.

Fill in the blanks with the correct yo form. Then translate the paragraph.

Yo __________ (*sacar*) la pelota del armario. Salí afuera y __________ (*empezar*) a rebotarla (*bounce it*) contra la pared (*wall*). "¿Dónde está Julio?" pensé. Pasó media hora. Pasaron cuarenta y cinco minutos. Al final me cansé de esperar, y __________ (*jugar*) solo.

# A Conjugation Celebration

Fill in the chart with the preterite tense forms of the verb **celebrar**. (And when you're done, you can celebrate.)

<table>
<tr><th>Person</th><th>Singular</th><th>Plural</th></tr>
<tr><td>1st</td><td>yo:</td><td>nosotros / as:</td></tr>
<tr><td>2nd</td><td>tú:</td><td rowspan="2">ustedes:<br>ellos:<br>ellas:</td></tr>
<tr><td>3rd</td><td>usted:<br>él:<br>ella:</td></tr>
</table>

# Preterite Pool

The following word pool has five hidden -ar verbs in the preterite tense. We've circled one for you. Can you find the others?

e s t u d i a m o s i h l k a d

p d é o j u g a s t e d m i o e

a v a d r f s i l w d p e h d j

s w b c o m p r a r o n p a j é

ó í o n r s r l n e n r m b p í

# Math + Spanish = Fun

Solve the following math problems. Write out the answers using Spanish number words. Remember that in Spanish, a period should be used to indicate thousands, rather than the comma used in English.

1.000 + 76 = ______________________________

1.000.000 – 100.000 = ______________________________

700 × 100 = ______________________________

2.000 + 250 = ______________________________

# Be Direct

According to the rules of grammar, pronouns replace nouns. **Direct object pronouns** replace direct object nouns.

Match the direct object pronouns in English with their Spanish equivalents

| | |
|---|---|
| ______ 1. me | a. nos |
| ______ 2. you | b. los |
| ______ 3. them | c. me |
| ______ 4. her | d. te |
| ______ 5. us | e. la |

# A Direct Objection

Fill in the chart below with the direct object pronouns.

| Person | Singular | Plural |
|---|---|---|
| 1st | | |
| 2nd | | Feminine:<br>Masculine: |
| 3rd | Feminine:<br>Masculine: | Feminine:<br>Masculine: |

# Speak Up, I Can't Hear You

Direct object pronouns have the same number and gender as the nouns they replace. They come before the verb.

Answer the following questions. In your answers, replace the nouns with direct object pronouns.

Iris, ¿tienes los discos compactos? ______________________

¿Dónde compraste los libros? ______________________

¿Necesitas la calculadora, Paco? ______________________

¿Puedes oírme? ______________________

¿Cuándo van a ver la película? ______________________

# Demonstrating Demonstrative Adjectives

**Demonstrative adjectives** point out or differentiate one group of items from another group. They are equivalent to the English words *this, that, these,* and *those.* Demonstrative adjectives also agree in number and gender with the nouns they accompany.

Which demonstrative adjective would you use to point out the following classroom objects to a friend?

- an eraser that's sitting in front of you: __________ borrador
- a dictionary that's on a bookshelf at the other end of the room: __________ diccionario
- a pencil that's sitting on the desk next to yours: __________ lápiz
- two pens in your hand: __________ plumas
- some maps that are on the wall furthest from you: __________ mapas
- a calculator in your lab partner's hand: __________ calculadora

# This, That, and the Other

Work with a partner. Use demonstrative adjectives to describe an object in your classroom. Then have your partner try to guess which object you're describing, based on your answers to his or her questions. For example, Este objeto está en la pared. ¿Qué es?

# Who's That Boy?

Match the demonstrative adjectives in English to their Spanish equivalents. Make sure you look carefully at the contexts provided. Don't forget that demonstrative adjectives must agree in number and in gender with the nouns they modify.

| | |
|---|---|
| ______ 1. that boy [at the other end of the library] | a. aquella |
| ______ 2. these compact disks [in my hand] | b. estos |
| ______ 3. that computer [that we saw in the store] | c. esta |
| ______ 4. this lesson [that we're doing right now] | d. esos |
| ______ 5. those papers [right over there] | e. aquel |

# Ach, My Whole Body Aches!

Answer the following questions with complete sentences. Remember the following:

- me duele + [singular noun]
- me duelen + [plural noun]

¿Qué te duele (*hurts you*) cuando no usas tus lentes (*eyeglasses*)? ____________

¿Qué te duele cuando comes demasiado (*too much*)? ____________

¿Qué te duele cuando juegas tenis por dos horas? ____________

¿Qué te duele cuando corres en una carrera (*race*)? ____________

¿Qué te duele cuando vas al dentista? ____________

# I Know a Great Little Peruvian Place

A direct object is the person or thing that receives the action of a verb. In Spanish, when the direct object of a verb is a person, you need to add an a after the verb. This is called the **personal** a.

Look at the following sentences. Is the personal a necessary? Rewrite each sentence on the line provided.

Don Francisco visita ______ el parque. ______________________________

Yo visito ______ Claudia. ______________________________

¿Conoces ______ mi hermano? ______________________________

Conozco ______ un buen restaurante peruano. ______________________________

Escuchan ______ el profesor dar su clase. ______________________________

¿Quieren escuchar ______ música? ______________________________

# Personal Statements

Write four sentences, using at least one of the following words per sentence (either the present or the preterite tense). Don't forget the personal a.

- buscar
- conocer
- ver
- llamar
- recordar
- visitar
- escuchar
- mirar

# Just Call Me Al Roker

To tell a friend to do something, you use the **informal command**. Regular tú commands use the same form as the third-person singular (él, ella) form of the present tense.

Based on the weather report you saw earlier, tell your friends and family what they need to do to prepare for the day using the prompts below.

Hace mucho calor en el carro. [abrir la ventana (*window*)]

Va a llover. [llevar el paraguas (*umbrella*)]

Hace mucho sol. [usar protector solar (*sunblock*)]

Hace much frío. [llevar un abrigo (*coat*)]

# Take a Swim in the Command Pool

The following word pool has five hidden tú commands. We've circled one for you. Can you find the others?

# Reflex Yourself

**Reflexive verbs** are verbs that tell us that the subject is doing something to himself or herself. Lavarse, for example, means *to wash oneself.*

Reflexive verbs always use a reflexive pronoun. List all of the reflexive pronouns, including singular and plural forms.

# I'll Answer Myself

Answer the following questions.

- What are two reflexive verbs that describe your daily routine?
- What are two reflexive stem-changing verbs?
- What are two reflexive verb + preposition expressions?
- What are two reflexive verbs that start with the letter *p*?

# *Cada Día, Yo....*

What do you do every morning? Fill out the schedule below in Spanish, based on your routine. Use reflexive verbs.

6:00 A.M. ______________________________

6:30 A.M. ______________________________

7:00 A.M. ______________________________

7:30 A.M. ______________________________

8:00 A.M. ______________________________

8:30 A.M. ______________________________

9:00 A.M. ______________________________

# Five Minutes a Day Keeps the Dentist Away

Work in groups of three. How many minutes does it take each of you to do the following activities? Fill out the chart.

| ¿En cuánto tiempo…? | Yo | Compañero 1 | Compañero 2 |
|---|---|---|---|
| te duchas | | | |
| te cepillas los dientes | | | |
| te vistes<br>te peinas | | | |
| te secas el pelo<br>te maquillas | | | |
| te afeitas | | | |

# Don't Bend Yourself Out of Shape

Most verbs in Spanish can be reflexive or nonreflexive, depending on the situation. If the verb acts on the subject, use the reflexive form. If the verb acts on something other than the subject, use the nonreflexive form. Which verb completes the sentences below? Choose the reflexive or nonreflexive form.

Yo _____ el carro ayer.
a. me lavé  b. lavé

Yo no _____ bien hoy.
a. me siento  b. siento

El peluquero (*hairdresser*) _____ mi cabello.
a. se corta  b. corta

Roberto _____ a las seis todos los días.
a. se levanta  b. levanta

La señora _____ a su bebé.
a. viste  b. se viste

¡Tú _____ muy fácilmente (*easily*), Frank!
a. enojas  b. te enojas

# Join Us at Pío Pío

Read the following advertisement. Then answer the questions that follow.

El pollo del Restaurante Pío Pío es más rico que
el pollo de otros restaurantes. El pollo al horno también tiene
menos grasa que el pollo en otros restaurantes.
Además es menos cara. ¡Te esperamos en Pío Pío!

- What is being compared in the advertisement?
- Name three comparisons in the advertisement.
- What words do the comparisons have in common?

# Stop Comparing Me to Others!

Spanish and English use comparisons to constrast people or things to one another. There are three kinds of comparisons: *equal to*, *greater than*, and *less than*.

Think about your naughtiest friend. Then think about your best-behaved friend. Write four comparative sentences in which you compare yourself to your two friends.

# As Cool as Catalina

Fill in the blanks with the correct comparative words. Use the cues in parentheses.

Emilia mira ________________ televisión que Cristina. (*more*)

Tú eres ________________ simpática que Catalina. (*less*)

No estudio ________________ tú. (*as much as*)

Conocen ________________ canciones que yo. (*more*)

Mis padres tienen ________________ dinero que mis tíos. (*less*)

Tu comes ________________ comida ________________ Ricardo. (*as much / as*)

# *The Ring* vs. *Meet the Fockers*

Write down the names of a horror flick and a comedy. Then come up with five sentences in Spanish that compare the two movies. Make sure you use the three kinds of comparisons: *more than*, *equal to*, and *less than*.

# Just Endings

Fill in the chart below with the correct verb endings for the preterite tense. Don't forget the accents!

| -er Verbs | -ar Verbs | -ir Verbs |
| --- | --- | --- |
| | | |

# Swimming in the Preterite

The word pool below has five hidden verbs in the preterite tense. We've circled one for you. Can you find the others?

| | | | | | | | | | | | | | | | |
|---|---|---|---|---|---|---|---|---|---|---|---|---|---|---|---|
| v | e | n | d | i | s | t | e | o | s | i | c | l | k | a | d |
| p | d | é | o | b | b | u | s | c | a | r | o | n | i | o | e |
| a | v | a | d | r | f | s | i | l | w | d | m | é | h | d | j |
| x | w | b | c | o | b | p | a | q | r | o | í | p | a | j | é |
| ó | í | c | e | r | r | ó | l | n | e | n | r | m | b | p | í |

# *Cristóbal Colón viajó a América en 1492.*

Think about your favorite historical period. Then write down five facts about that time period in Spanish, using the same form as the title above. Can't remember any facts? Write down five recent events that you think will go down in history. Be sure to use the correct preterite forms.

# The Dog Ate My Homework

Using a word or phrase from each of the columns below, form sentences that explain what you and others did at some point in the past. Create at least four sentences. Be sure to use the correct preterite form.

| Subject | Verb | Time in the Past |
| --- | --- | --- |
| yo<br>tú<br>mi amiga Raquel Franchesca<br>el profesor de biología<br>el cachorro (*puppy*)<br>la vecina (*neighbor*) | tocar el piano<br>comer una hamburguesa<br>romperse la pierna<br>comer mi tarea<br>dar una prueba<br>regar (*water*) las plantas<br>estudiar mucho | ayer<br>esta mañana<br>el año pasado<br>el fin de semana anterior<br>hace tres días |

# A Day in the Life of Fido

Put yourself in your pet's shoes. What does she or he do while you're at school all day? **¿Tu pero se aburre?** (*Does your dog get bored?*) Write five sentences describing Fido or Fluffy's day-to-day activities. If you don't have a pet, imagine what a dog, cat, fish, or bird might do while its owners are gone.

Remember: reflexive verbs describe actions a person does to himself or herself. Reflexive verbs are conjugated just like any other preterite-tense verbs, but they must include reflexive pronouns.

# It's All in the Past

Put your conjugation knowledge to the test. Fill in the blanks with the correct conjugations of the verbs below.

Third-person plural of escribir: ______________________________

First-person singular of cerrar: ______________________________

Second-person singular of volver: ______________________________

First-person singular of salir: ______________________________

Second-person plural of comer: ______________________________

First-person singular of oír: ______________________________

# *Los Días de Nuestras Vidas*

Imagine you work for a Spanish-speaking television station. It's your job to suggest show titles to the producer. Come up with a catchy title in Spanish for each of the following types of television shows.

- la telenovela
- el noticiero
- los dibujos animados
- el documental
- la propaganda
- el programa deportivo
- el pronóstico del tiempo
- el programa de entrevistas

# Now Playing: *Invasión Extraterrestre*

Imagine you work for a low-budget movie production house. It's your job to suggest movie titles to the producer. Come up with unusual Spanish names for each of the following movies: a sci-fi flick, a horror movie, a western, a romantic comedy, and an adventure film.

# I Indirectly Object

**Indirect object pronouns** replace indirect object nouns.

Fill in the chart below with the correct indirect object pronouns.

| Person | Singular | Plural |
|---|---|---|
| 1st | | |
| 2nd | | |
| 3rd | | |

# To Me, To You, To Her, To Them

How well do you know the indirect object pronouns? Use the cues in the parentheses to figure out the indirect object pronoun for each sentence. Write the pronoun in the space provided.

Juan ________________ escribe una carta. (*to his parents*)

La niña ________________ canta en español. (*to us*)

La profesora ________________ enseña los verbos. (*to me*)

Nosotras ________________ compramos un suéter rojo. (*for her*)

Yo ________________ doy mi opinión solamente. (*to you, informal*)

# Shopaholics Anonymous

Imagine your cousin is a shopoholic. Every time your cousin goes shopping, he ends up buying gifts for everyone. Use the prompts below to write five sentences about what your cousin bought for each person. Make sure you use indirect object pronouns.

mis hermanos / diez discos compactos ____________________

yo / un anillo de oro (*a gold ring*) ____________________

su hija / una muñeca de porcelana (*porcelain doll*) ____________________

yo y Juan / un libro nuevo ____________________

su esposo / un abrigo de lana (*wool coat*) ____________________

# Direct or Indirect?

Which sentences require the direct object pronoun? Which require the indirect object pronoun? Choose the correct answer for each of the sentences below. For an extra challenge, you can also fill in the blank with the correct object pronoun.

Irina compra una hamburguesa. Irina ________ compra.
a. direct object pronoun  b. indirect object pronoun

Doy la calculadora a mi compañero. ________ doy la calculadora.
a. direct object pronoun  b. indirect object pronoun

Mauricio ve a Federico. Mauricio ________ ve.
a. direct object pronoun  b. indirect object pronoun

Mando un postal (*postcard*) a mi hermana. ________ mando un postal.
a. direct object pronoun  b. indirect object pronoun

Marible tiene la llave. Maribel ________ tiene.
a. direct object pronoun  b. indirect object pronoun

# I Command You to Be Irregular

There are eight verbs that have irregular tú commands. List as many of these verbs as you can. If you have trouble, use this mneumonic device to jog your memory: SHIP'S TV.

# *Ven a Nueva York*

Imagine your Argentinian penpal wants to visit the United States. What advice will you give him or her? Write four tú commands. Use the following verbs: ir, venir, hacer, and poner.

# All Orders

Your mom is so bossy! She gives you order after order. Fill in the blanks below with the correct tú commands. Use the verbs in parentheses.

¡__________ cuidado con el cuchillo! (*tener*)

__________ tus tareas, por favor. (*hacer*)

__________ los platos en la mesa. (*poner*)

__________ a tu cuarto ahora mismo. (*ir*)

¡__________ aquí! (*venir*)

# Do This, Do That

Imagine you're telling your little brother what chores he needs to do this weekend. Make tú commands out of the following phrases. Replace each noun with a pronoun.

Remember: in an affirmative command, the pronoun is always attached to the end of the verb.

barrer el piso (*sweep the floor*): ______________________________

cortar el césped (*lawn*): ______________________________

sacar la basura: ______________________________

limpiar el baño: ______________________________

hacer las camas: ______________________________

# Don't Go There, That Place Is a Dump

A **superlative** expresses the highest or lowest degree of a quality. To form superlatives, use the following constructions:

- [definite article] + [noun] + más + [adjective] + de
- [definite article] + [noun] + menos + [adjective] + de

Answer the following questions in Spanish. Use complete sentences.

What is the most elegant restaurant in your city or town? ____________________

What is the least elegant restaurant in your city or town? ____________________

What is the most beautiful city in the world? ____________________

What is the least beautiful city in the world? ____________________

# It Might Be Irregular, but It's Still the Best

As with comparatives, there are also irregular superlatives.

Fill out the chart below with as many irregular forms as you can think of.

| Adjective | Comparison | Superlative |
| --- | --- | --- |
| | | |

# The Best and the Worst

Conduct a survey among three people in your Spanish class. Ask them the following questions in Spanish. Your classmates should answer in complete sentences.

¿Cuál es el mejor grupo musical del mundo?

¿Cuál es el peor grupo musical del mundo?

¿Quién es la mejor película del año?

¿Quién es la peor película del año?

¿Cuál es el mejor programa de televisión?

¿Cuál es el peor programa de televisión?

# Anywhere a Cat Can Go

A **preposition** expresses the relationship between things in terms of time or place. Prepositions answer questions like *where*? and *when*? Spanish prepositions include **sobre** (*over*), **en** (*in*), and **hasta** (*until*).

One of the most common prepositions in the Spanish language is **a**. List three uses for **a** and give an example of each.

# For Whom....

The prepositions **para** and **por** can both be translated as *for*. However, they have very different uses in Spanish.

Write four sentences: two that use **para** correctly and two that use **por** correctly.

# Butter Was Made for Bread

Is it por or para? Choose the correct *for* preposition for each sentence below.

Mando un mensaje a Arturo ________ correo electrónico (*email*).
a. para    b. por

La mantequilla (*butter*) es ________ el pan.
a. para    b. por

La caja es ________ los lápices.
a. para    b. por

Vengo ________ ti a las nueve, ¿está bien?
a. para    b. por

# Portable *Por*

Below are some uses of por and para. Decide which use belongs to which preposition.

- Indicates a deadline
- Indicates the recipient of something
- Indicates the means by which something is done (i.e., by telephone, by email, etc.)
- Indicates a destination
- Indicates the duration of an action
- Indicates the motive for an action

# *Fuimos a la Playa Para el Sol*

Make three sentences from the following words and phrases, using the title above as a model. Choose one word or phrase from each column, adding **por** or **para** where necessary.

| Verb | Place | Reason or Method | Reason or Method |
|---|---|---|---|
| fui | a la biblioteca | carro | estudiar |
| fuimos | a la playa | comprar fruta | tomar sol |
|  | al supermercado | estudiar | mi mamá |

# Dedicated *De*

Another common preposition in the Spanish language is de (*of*). List three uses for de and give an example of each.

# Give Me a Break

The Spanish verb dar (*to give*) has an irregular past tense. Fill in the blanks below, using the correct conjugation of dar.

The first-person plural preterite form is ______________.

The second-person singular informal preterite form is ______________.

The third-person singular preterite form is ______________.

The second-person plural preterite form is ______________.

The first-person singular preterite form is ______________.

# Know Thy Tenses

Fill in the chart below with the preterite tense forms of saber (*to know*). Don't forget that saber has a stem change in the preterite.

<table>
<tr><th>Person</th><th>Singular</th><th>Plural</th></tr>
<tr><td>1st</td><td>yo:</td><td>nosotros / as:</td></tr>
<tr><td>2nd</td><td>tú:</td><td rowspan="2">ustedes:<br>ellos:<br>ellas:</td></tr>
<tr><td>3rd</td><td>usted:<br>él:<br>ella:</td></tr>
</table>

# The Past Is Past

The preterite forms of ir and ser are irregular. However, you won't need to memorize two separate conjugations, because the forms are identical. Context tells us which of the two verbs is being used.

Make four sentences out of the words and phrases below. Choose one from each column, using the appropriate preterite form.

| Subject | Verb | Place, Adjective, or Noun |
|---|---|---|
| yo<br>tú<br>mis primos (*cousins*)<br>mi abuelo | ir<br>ser | a la escuela<br>estudiantes<br>en carro<br>médico |

# Last Summer, We Went to....

Write a five-sentence paragraph about a vacation spot you've visited recently. Use the preterite form of **ir** as many times as you can. Try to use both the singular and plural forms.

# Seeing Is Believing

Fill in the blanks with the correct preterite form of the verb ver. Don't forget that it's irregular.

Anoche yo y Josefina ______________ la película *Y Tu Mamá También*.

Antonio, ¿ ______________ ese carro? ¡Es el nuevo Porche!

Doña Fernanda ______________ caer el vaso, pero no pudo salvarlo.

Mis padres ______________ un perro callejero (*stray*) en nuestro barrio.

Yo ______________ una cucaracha en la cocina. ¡Qué asco!

# Who's Doing What When?

In English, *to be* and the present participle (the *-ing* form) are used to express an action that is in progress. Spanish has a similar construction: the **present progressive**. To form the present progressive, follow this construction:

[the present tense of *estar*] + [the present participle (verb stem + *-ando* or *-iendo*)]

Think about the following people. What do you think they're doing right now? Write complete sentences using the present progressive.

tus primos (*cousins*): ____________________

tu mejor amigo: ____________________

Justin Timberlake: ____________________

tu abuela: ____________________

las gemelas (*twins*) Olsen: ____________________

# And Now the Brat Is....

Imagine you're baby-sitting your neighbors' two-year-old. This kid is a real nightmare—you'll think twice before you agree to baby-sit again. You decide to call your best friend to vent about your misfortune. What do you tell him or her? Write four creative sentences in Spanish about what the kid is doing right now. Use the present progressive.

# Preferring, Feeling, Sleeping

Most verbs have regular present participles. To form regular past participles, just add -ando or -iendo to the stem, depending on the verb ending. For example: hablar, hablando; comer, comiendo; and vivir, viviendo. Others have irregular present participles. Unfortunately, you'll have to memorize the irregular past participles.

Write down the present participle form for each of the following verbs.

preferir: ______

sentir: ______

conseguir: ______

pedir: ______

seguir: ______

dormir: ______

# Señor López Speaks So Slowly

**Adverbs** modify verbs, adjectives, or other adverbs. There are several kinds of adverbs in Spanish. The easiest adverbs are those that end in -mente. Think of -mente as equivalent to -*ly* in English. To form a -mente adverb, simply add -mente to the feminine form of the adjective. For example, lento, lentamente; and fácil, fácilmente.

Think about your favorite teacher. First write down three adjectives that describe him or her. Next turn those adjectives into adverbs. Now use these adverbs to write three sentences about your teacher.

# Before or After?

An adverb precedes the adjective it modifies but normally follows the verb it modifies.

Unscramble the following sentences, listing all of the possibilities. Pay close attention to adverb placement.

cocina / abuela / maravillosamente / mi

en la computadora / me gusta / jugar / mucho

siempre / ocupada / la profesora / está

lentamente / caminas / muy

un poco / estoy / cansada / hoy

# I Always Sleep in Class

Work in groups of three. How often do you and your classmates do the following activities? Fill out the chart with the following adverbs: con mucha frecuencia, de vez en cuando, casi nunca, and nunca.

| Actividadas | Yo | Compañero 1 | Compañero 2 |
|---|---|---|---|
| mirar la televisión | | | |
| dormir en clase | | | |
| estudiar | | | |
| ir a la biblioteca | | | |
| lavar los platos | | | |

# Where? Here!

¿**Dónde?** adverbs answer the question *where*? These adverbs are also called **adverbs of place**.

Write down as many ¿**Dónde?** adverbs as you can.

# Dive in Cautiously

The following word pool has five hidden ¿Cuándo? adverbs. We've circled one for you. Can you find the others?

| | | | | | | | | | | | | | | | |
|---|---|---|---|---|---|---|---|---|---|---|---|---|---|---|---|
| a | n | o | c | h | e | y | ñ | u | p | i | h | l | k | a | h |
| p | d | é | o | d | e | s | p | u | é | s | d | m | i | o | o |
| a | v | a | d | r | f | s | i | l | w | d | p | é | h | d | y |
| s | w | b | t | e | m | p | r | a | n | o | i | p | a | j | é |
| m | a | ñ | a | n | a | r | l | n | e | n | r | m | b | p | í |

# A Parallel Past

You already know how to use the preterite tense to express actions and events in the past. The preterite, as you know, is used to express actions that are finished or completed. Leí el libro. (*I read the book.*)

The **imperfect** is the second kind of simple past. In contrast to the preterite, the imperfect expresses actions or events that are continuous or habitual in the past. Viajaba en España. (*I was traveling in Spain.*)

Fill out the two columns below with the imperfect tense endings for each type of verb.

| -er Verbs | -ar Verbs | -ir Verbs |
|---|---|---|
| | | |

# Irregularity's Triple Threat

There are only three verbs that have irregular forms in the imperfect tense. Which ones are they? Write them down and then come up with a creative way to remember them.

# Answers

1. Answers will vary but might include: *armadillo*, *coyote*, *taco*, *tamale*, *tango*, *mariachi*, *amigo*, *hasta la vista*, or *adiós*.

2. Translations should resemble this one: *Hi! I'm cecili@89.... my friends call me "la Ceci." I'm an intelligent and serious person—but I'm also very social. I have lots of friends. My true passion is art—everyone tells me that I'm super creative. Painting is fascinating to me [I love to paint]! One day I'll be famous. Do you want to chat with me? Go for it....*

3. biblioteca, *not* librería; tela, *not* fábrica; jabón, *not* sopa; grabar, *not* recordar; alfombra, *not* carpeta

4. *(Taurus: Your financial matters require your immediate attention. Things are stable now, but a tornado is about to come. Prepare yourself.)* Cognates are bolded:
   *Tauro: Los asuntos de tus* ***financias requieren*** *de tu* ***inmediata atención****. Las cosas están* ***estables*** *por ahora, pero un* ***tornado*** *está por venir.* ***Prepárate****.*

5. Answers will vary.

6. (*Spell it out*)
   aburrido (*bored*), guapo (*cute*), clase de español (*Spanish class*), almuerzo (*lunch*)

7. Answers are as follows: general: heh-neh-RAHL, *not* djeh-neh-RAHL; zapato: ssah-PAH-toh, *not* zah-PAH-toh; observa: ohb-SEHR-va, *not* ohb-ZUR-vah; señora: seh-NYOH-rah, *not* she-NOH-rah; piña: PEE-nyah, *not* PEE-nah; calle: CAH-yeh, *not* CAH-lleh; hambre: AHM-breh, *not* HAHM-breh

8. Stressed syllables are underlined. Había una vez un hombre tan pequeño que se subió encima de una canica y dijo, "¡El mundo es mío!" Había una vez un señor tan perezoso que soñó que estaba trabajando y amaneció cansado.

9. Answers will vary but might include *hola*, *buenos días*, *buenas tardes*, *buenas noches* (for "hello"); *chau*, *hasta luego*, *hasta mañana*, *adios*, *nos vemos* (for "good-bye").

10. buenos días
    hasta mañana
    chau
    hola
    buenas tardes

11. Molly: ¡Hola! Me llamo Molly.
    Theo: Mucho gusto, Molly.
    Molly: ¿Cómo te llamas?
    Theo: Me llamo Theo.

12. b b
 a a

13. Answers will vary.

14. Answers will vary.

15. La comida en la cafetería es asquerosa. / Es asquerosa la comida en la cafetería. (*The food in the cafeteria is disgusting.*)
 Su novio es el capitán del equipo de fútbol. / El capitán del equipo de fútbol es su novio. (*Her boyfriend is the captain of the soccer team.*)
 Me gusta la pizza fría. / La pizza me gusta fría. (*I like cold pizza.*)

16. enero, febrero, marzo, abril, mayo, junio, julio, agosto, septiembre, octubre, noviembre, diciembre; diciembre, noviembre, octubre, septiembre, agosto, julio, junio, mayo, abril, marzo, febrero, enero

17. Answers will vary.

18. Answers will vary.

19. Answers will vary.

20. Answers will vary.

21. Son las tres de la mañana.
    Son las dos de la tarde.
    Es la una de la mañana.
    Son las diez de la noche.
    Son las cinco de la tarde.

22. Answers will vary.

23. The clock should say 4:50.
    The clock should say 12:30.
    The clock should say 1:15.
    The clock should say 3:00.
    The clock should say 7:15.

24. (1) e
    (2) d
    (3) b
    (4) c
    (5) a

25. Answers might include: *química*, *inglés*, *español*, *historia*, *biología*, or *geografía*.

26. (*Translate the following instructions.*)
    True or false?

Answer the questions.
Interview a classmate.
Work in teams.
Complete the sentences.

27. Julieta: ¿Me amas, Romeo? / Me amas, Romeo.
    Romeo: ¡No puedo vivir sin ti! / No, puedo vivir sin ti.

    Señor Tengomucho: ¿Tienes un dólar? / Tienes un dólar.
    Señor Nolatengo: ¡No tengo 25 centavos! / No, tengo veinticinco centavos.

    Fulanito: ¿Quieres ir a la discoteca? / Quieres ir a la discoteca.
    Fulanita: No me parece mala idea. / No, me parece mala idea.

    Mamá: No estás feliz, Jaimito. / ¿No estás feliz, Jaimito?
    Jaimito: No estoy feliz. / ¡No, estoy feliz!

28. Answers will vary.

29. vehr ehs cre-HER
    dehl DEE-choh ahl EH-choh ahy oon grahn TREH-cho
    ah dee-AH-ree-oh OO-nah mahn-SSAH-nah ehs COH-sah SAH-nah
    CAH-dah LOH-coh cohn soo TEH-mah

30. Answers will vary.

31. 1st: yo, nosotros, nosotras
    2nd: tú, usted, ustedes
    3rd: él, ella, ellos, ellas

32. Use *tú* with: your classmate, your dad, and the five-year-old child. Use *usted* with: the hotel clerk, the bus driver, and a museum guard.

33. él, yo, ella, tú, nosotras, usted, ellos, ustedes

34. soy, eres, es, somos, sois, son

35. Answers will vary.

36. Answers will vary.

37. Answers will vary.

38. Answers will vary.

39. (*I sing like a dying cat.*)
    Do you study every night?
    Do you draw well?
    Do you sing well?
    Do you listen to rap music?
    Do you talk a lot in class?

40. ellos / ellas llegan
yo viajo
tú hablas
nosotros / nosotras escuchamos
ustedes dibujan
el / ella compra

41. ellos / ellas bailan, ustedes bailan, nosotros / nosotras bailamos, el / ella / usted baila, tú bailas, yo bailo

42. Masculine: cuaderno, libro, poema, león, sabor; feminine: mano, foto, miel, mesa, profesora

43. dos manos
un lápiz
dos problemas
una nacionalidad
dos países
una palabra

44. Answers will vary.

45. *día*: masculine; broken rule: "Nouns that end in *-a* are feminine."
*radio*: feminine; broken rule: "Nouns that end in *-o* are masculine."
*sal*: feminine; broken rule: "Nouns that end in *-l* are masculine."
*planeta*: masculine; broken rule: "Nouns that end in *-a* are feminine."

*moto*: feminine; broken rule: "Nouns that end in *-o* are masculine."
*piel:* feminine; broken rule: "Nouns that end in *-l* are masculine."

46. unos
    una
    un
    unas

47. un
    los
    la
    unas

48. ¿Max habla español? ¿Habla Max español? Max habla español, ¿verdad?

49. Answers include: Who? = *¿Quién*?, What? = *¿Qué*?, Which ones? = *¿Cuáles*?, When? = *¿Cuándo*?, How? = *¿Cómo*?, Why? = *¿Por qué*?, How much? = *¿Cuánto*?

50. Conversa con sus amigas ...
    Descanso ...
    Regresamos a la escuela ...
    Estudiamos el español ...

51. Answers will vary, but questions should be constructed as follows:
    *¿Juegas al póquer*?

¿*Acampas en las montañas*?
¿*Montas a caballo*?
¿*Buceas en el mar*?

52. el otoño
 la primavera
 el verano
 el invierno

53. Answers will vary but might include: *comer* (to eat), *beber* (to drink), *defender* (to defend), *oler* (to smell), *parecer* (to seem, to appear), and *correr* (to run).

54. Answers will vary but might include: *Como unos cereales y bebo jugo de naranja para el desayuno.* (I eat some cereal and drink orange juice for breakfast.)

55. Answers will vary.

56. yo discuto, tú discutes, usted / él / ella discute, nosotros discutimos, ustedes / ellos / ellas discuten

57. Answers will vary.

58. Julia y Mari van al centro comercial.
 Tú vas al partido de fútbol.
 Nosotros vamos a la escuela.

Yo voy al circo.
Ustedes van al restaurante.

59. Answers will vary but might include: *Van a ir de pesca* and *Van a pasear en bote*.

60. la tienda
la escuela / la oficina
el estadio
la biblioteca
el mercado / el supermercado

61. a b
a b

62. Teodoro nunca come vegetales.
The sentence is grammatically correct.
Ustedes toman jugo de naranja en la mañana.
The sentence is grammatically correct.

63. Yo estudio matemáticas y tú estudias arte.
Los niños son estudiantes y la mujer es profesora.
Nosotros vamos a la playa y ustedes van a las montañas.

64. Answers will vary but might include: *Como unas frutas todos los días. A veces como el maíz. Nunca como el pez.* (I eat some fruit every day. Sometimes I eat corn. I never eat fish.)

65. Answers will vary.

66. nosotros volvemos
ustedes duermen
él / ella puede
ellos encuentran

67. Daniela cierra el libro de química, y comienza a llorar. ¡No entiendo! dice. ¡No quiero perder el año! (*Daniela closes the chemistry book and starts to cry. "I don't get it!" she says. "I don't want to flunk out this year!"*)

68. yo repito, tú repites, usted / él / ella repite, nosotros repetimos, ustedes / ellos / ellas repiten

69. (1) f
(2) d
(3) a
(4) e
(5) b
(6) c

70. Answers will vary, but answers should begin as follows:
*Mi madre se llama …*
*Su música favorita es …*
*Mi postre favorito es …*
*Sus nombres son …*

71. Answers will vary.

72. Answers will vary.

73. c  b
a  c

74. (1) d
(2) e
(3) f
(4) b
(5) c
(6) a

75. buena
malo
gran
buen
grande
mal

76. My teacher is a great woman.
My teacher is a large woman.

Jorge's an old friend.
Jorge's a friend who's old (as in *elderly*).
The poor (as in *unfortunate*) boy is lost.
The poor (as in *having no money*) boy is lost.

77. salgo
traigo
hago
pongo

78. Answers will vary.

79. Answers will vary but might include:
*Hace calor. / Hace sol.*
*Hace viento. / Hace frío. / Hace fresco.*
*Hace viento. / Hace frío. / Hace fresco.*
*Hace calor. / Hace sol.*

80. Answers will vary.

81. Florida cien, Florida State ochenta y dos
Stanford setenta y ocho, UCLA setenta y siete
Princeton sesenta y siete, Harvard cincuenta y seis
Kentucky noventa y ocho, Tennessee setenta y cuatro
Vanderbilt ochenta y ocho, Virginia ochenta y cinco
Purdue noventa y uno, Indiana setenta y cinco

82. yo conozco, tú conoces, usted / él / ella conoce, nosotros conocemos, ustedes / ellos ellas conocen

83. (*It seems like you're going to lose*)
ellos / ellas parecen
yo conduzco
tú ofreces
yo traduzco
ustedes conocen
yo parezco

84. (1) c, ofrezco
(2) d, conduzco
(3) b, conozco
(4) a, traduzco

85. Ella es americana.
Él es italiano.
Ella es mexicana.
Él es chino.
Él es hindú.

86. Answers will vary.

87. Answers will vary.

88. yo estoy, nosotros estamos, tú estás, ustedes están, él / ella está, ellos / ellas están

89. Answers should include: *to express location*, *to talk about health*, and *to talk about well being*.

90. Answers will vary.

91. Answers will vary.

92. b c<br>a c

93. Answers will vary.

94. la computadora suya<br>mis llaves<br>la cámara tuya<br>nuestro carro<br>la televisión mía<br>nuestra casa

95. (1) b<br>(2) d<br>(3) a<br>(4) c

96. The first sentence states that *the boy is smart*. The second sentence states that *the boy is ready.*
    The first sentence states that that *Carolina is boring*. The second sentence states that *Carolina is bored*.
    The first sentence states that *the cat is lively*. The second sentence states that *the cat is alive*.
    The first sentence states that the *apple is green*. The second sentence states that *the apple is not ripe*.

97. Answers will vary.

98. Answers will vary.

99. Answers will vary but might include:
    *Deportes*: *hockey, béisbol, baloncesto*
    *Personas*: *jugador, aficionado, beisbolista*
    *Lugares*: *piscina, parque, estadio*

100. Answers will vary.

101. yo sé, tú sabes, usted / él / ella sabe, nosotros / as sabemos, ustedes / ellos / elas saben

102. Answers will vary but might include: *Hago invitaciones* and *Compañero 1 saca fotos*.

103. Answers will vary.

104. sabe
     sabemos

sabes
saben
sé

105. *Saber* means "to know a fact / piece of information" or "to know how to do something." *Conocer* means "to know a person, place, or thing."

106. Answers will vary but might include: *Paris Hilton no sabe actuar* (Paris Hilton doesn't know how to act), *Tú conoces a mi mejor amigo* (You know my best friend), and so on.

107. b a
b a

108. Answers will vary but might include: *Tú tomas el autobus* (You take the bus), *Ustedes llevan los libros a clase* (You all bring the books to class), and so on.

109. *Tomar* means "to take something" or "to drink something." *Llevar* means "to take someone or something away."

110. tomamos
llevo
tomar
llevar
tomas
llevan

111. Matthew pregunta qué hora es.
Tengo sueño. Pido una taza de café.
¡Mi hermano no tiene dinero! Me pide cinco dólares.
Mi amigo pregunta dónde está el baño.

112. Answers will vary but might include: *Eric Clapton toca la guitarra. Tú no juegas al golf.*

113. Top half: *la camiseta*, *la chaqueta*, *la sudadera*
Bottom half: *la falda*, *los pantalones*, *los calcetines*

114. Answers will vary but might include: *Frances lleva pantalones azules. Marta lleva una bufanda amarilla.*

115. Es de colores rojo, blanco, y azul.
Es de color marrón / café.
Es de colores blanco, amarillo, y verde.
Es de color azul.

116. Max compró un póster de The Strokes.
Yo compré una colonia de Armani.
Mis hermanos compraron unos discos compactos.
Tú compraste un juego de computadora.
Tú y Bianca compraron unas blusas de última moda.

117. Yo saqué la pelota del armario. Salí afuera, y empecé a rebotarla contra la pared. "¿Dónde está Julio?" pensé. Pasó media hora. Pasaron cuarenta y cinco minutos. Al final me cansé de esperar, y jugué solo. (*I took the ball out of the closet. I went outside and began to bounce it against the wall. "Where is Julio?" I thought. A half hour passed. Forty-five minutes passed. Finally I got tired of waiting, and I played by myself.*)

118. yo celebré, tú celebraste, usted / él / ella celebró, nosotros / as celebramos, ustedes / ellos / ellas celebraron

119.

e s t u d i a m o s i h l k a d
p d é o j u g a s t e d m i o e
a v a d r f s i l w d p e h d j
s w b c o m p r a r o n p a j é
ó í o n r s r l n e n r m b p í

120. 1.076: mil setenta y seis
900.000: novecientos mil
70.000: setenta mil
2.250: dos mil dos cientos cinquenta

121. (1) c
(2) d
(3) b
(4) e
(5) a

122. 1st: me, nos
2nd: te, la / lo
3rd: la / lo, las / los

123. Answers will vary but might include:
*No, no los tengo.*
*Los compré en la librería.*
*Sí, la necesito.*
*No, no te oigo.*
*La vamos a ver mañana.*

124. este borrador
aquel diccionario
ese lápiz
estas plumas
aquellos mapas
esa calculadora

125. Answers will vary but might include:
  a. *Este objeto está en la pared. ¿Qué es?*
  b. *¿Es un mapa?*
  a. *¡Sí!*

126. (1) e
  (2) b
  (3) a
  (4) c
  (5) d

127. Me duelen los ojos.
  Me duele la barriga / panza. / Me duele el estómago.
  Me duele el brazo.
  Me duelen las piernas.
  Me duelen los dientes. / Me duele la boca.

128. Don Francisco visita el parque.
  Yo visito a Claudia.
  ¿Conoces a mi hermano?
  Conozco un buen restauranto peruano.
  Escuchan al profesor dar su clase.
  ¿Quieren escuchar música?

129. Answers will vary but might include: *Busco a mi amigo. / Busco un diccionario nuevo. Veo tus fotos. / Veo una chica guapa.*

130. ¡Abre la ventana!
¡Lleva el paraguas!
¡Usa protector solar!
¡Lleva un abrigo!

131.

a l r l a c i s t o v u e l v e
t j n l s t l n s p b z a r z l
o s m e n s c o m p r a t e q p
c h j v e r b e a o g w l s n o
a n a a z h r o p c a m b i a m

132. Singular: yo me, tú te, él se / ella se / usted se
Plural: nosotros nos / nosotras nos, ellos se / ellas se / ustedes se

133. Answers will vary but might include:
*levantarse, lavarse*
*despertarse, probarse*

*acordarse de, burlarse de*
*ponerse, peinarse*

134. Answers will vary but might include: *A las 6:30 me levanto. A las 7:00 me cepillo los dientes. A las 7:30 me ducho.*

135. Answers will vary but might include: *Yo me ducho en diez minutos. Rob se ducha en quince minutos. Amber se ducha en veinte minutos.*

136. b a
a a
b b

137. (Translation of advertisement: *The chicken at Restaurante Pío Pío is tastier than the chicken at other restaurants. The baked chicken is less greasy than the chicken at other restaurants. It's also less expensive. We're waiting for you to join us at Pío Pío!*)
The chicken at Pío Pío and the chicken in other restaurants
*El pollo del Restaurante Pío Pío es más rico que el pollo de otros restaurantes / El pollo al horno también tiene menos grasa que el pollo en otros restaurantes.*
*más, menos*

138. Answers will vary but might include: *Yo soy menos travieso que mi amigo. Yo soy más bueno que mi amiga.*

139. más
menos
tanto como
más
menos
tanta ... como

140. Answers will vary but might include: Meet the Fockers *es más gracioso que* The Ring. Meet the Fockers *es menos espantoso que* The Ring. Meet the Fockers *es tan estúpido como* The Ring.

141. -er: í, iste, ió, imos, ieron
-ar: é, aste, ó, amos, aron
-ir: í, iste, ió, imos, ieron

142.

| | | | | | | | | | | | | | | | |
|---|---|---|---|---|---|---|---|---|---|---|---|---|---|---|---|
| v | e | n | d | i | s | t | e | o | s | i | c | l | k | a | d |
| p | d | é | o | b | b | u | s | c | a | r | o | n | i | o | e |
| a | v | a | d | r | f | s | i | l | w | d | m | é | h | d | j |
| x | w | b | c | o | b | p | a | q | r | o | í | p | a | j | é |
| ó | í | c | e | r | r | ó | l | n | e | n | r | m | b | p | í |

Circled: vendiste, buscaron, comí, dejé, cerró

143. Answers will vary but might include: *Cristóbal Colón viajó a América. Napoleón Bonaparte nació en Francia.*

144. Answers will vary but might include: *Yo toqué el piano ayer. La vecina regó las plantas esta mañana.*

145. Answers will vary but might include: *Esta mañana me levanté a las dos de la tarde. Comí un hueso y volvé a dormir.*

146. ellos / ellas escribieron
yo cerré
tú volviste
yo salí
ustedes comieron
yo oí

147. Answers will vary.

148. Answers will vary but might include: *Invasión Extraterrestre* and *Justicia de Vaqueros.*

149. 1st: me, nos
2nd: te / le, les
3rd: le, les

150. les
nos

me
le
te

151. Les compró diez discos compactos.
Me compró un anillo de oro.
Le compró una muñeca de porcelana.
Nos compró un libro nuevo.
Le compró un abrigo de lana.

152. a (la)
b (le)
a (lo)
b (le)
a (la)

153. salir, hacer, ir, poner, ser, tener, venir, decir

154. Answers will vary but might include: *Ve al consulado* (consulate) *de los Estados Unidos. Ven para mi cumpleaños. Haz las maletas temprano. Pon los documentos en tu mochila*.

155. Ten
Haz
Pon

Ve
Ven

156. Bárrelo.
Córtalo.
Sácala.
Límpialo.
Hazlas.

157. Answers will vary but might include:
*Nápoli es el restaurante más elegante de la ciudad.*
*McDonald's es el restaurante menos elegante de la ciudad.*
*San Francisco es la ciudad más bonita del mundo.*
*Guayaquil es la ciudad menos bonita del mundo.*

158. Answers will vary but might include: *bueno, mejor, el mejor*; *malo, peor, el peor*; *grande, mayor, el mayor*; *joven, menor, el menor.*

159. Answers will vary but might include: *The Killers es el mejor grupo musical del mundo.* The *Backstreet Boys es el peor grupo musical del mundo.* Million Dollar Baby *es la mejor película del año.* War of the Worlds *es la peor película del año. 24 es el mejor programa de televisión.* The Surreal Life *es el peor programa de televisión.*

160. Answers will vary but might include: (1) to introduce an indirect object, *Doy la pluma a mi compañero*; (2) to show movement towards something, *Vamos a la escuela*; and (3) to show distance, *Mi casa está a una cuadra.*

161. Answers will vary but might include:
*Mi papá trabaja para una compañía alemana.*
*Compré un regalo para mi hermano.*
*¡José maneja a 100 kilómetros por hora!*
*Estuve en Francia por un mes.*

162. b
a
a
b

163. *Por*: duration of an action, motive for an action
*Para*: deadline, recipient, destination

164. Answers will vary but might include:
*Fui / fuimos a la biblioteca por carro para estudiar.*
*Fui / fuimos a la playa por dos días para tomar sol.*
*Fui / fuimos al supermercado para comprar fruta para mi mamá.*

165. Answers will vary but might include: (1) to show possession, *La camisa es de Marta*; (2) to show origin, *Soy de Madrid*; and (3) to show what something is made of, *La muñeca es de porcelana.*

166. (nosotros) dimos
(tú) diste
(él / ella) dio
(ustedes) dieron
(yo) di

167. yo supe, tú supiste, usted / él / ella supieron, nosotros / as supimos, ustedes / ellos / ellas supieron

168. Answers will vary but might include:
*Yo fui a la escuela.*
*Tú fuiste en carro.*
*Mis primos fueron estudiantes.*
*Mi abuelo fue médico.*

169. Answers will vary but might include: *El año pasado yo y mi familia fuimos a Madrid. Fuimos a muchos museos, y fuimos también a un mercado al aire fresco. Fui con mi hermana a una discoteca y bailamos toda la noche.*

170. vimos
viste

vio
vieron
vi

171. Answers will vary but might include:
*Están comiendo.*
*Está durmiendo.*
*Está actuando.*
*Está cantando.*
*Están bailando.*

172. Answers will vary but might include: *El niño está llorando. El niño está rompiendo sus juguetes. El niño está escribiendo en las paredes. El niño está corriendo en la cocina.*

173. prefiriendo
sintiendo
consiguiendo
pidiendo
siguiendo
durmiendo

174. Answers will vary but might include:
*inteligente, inteligentemente*: *Mi profesor responde inteligentamente a mis preguntas.*
*fabuloso, fabulosamente*: *Él se viste fabulosamente.*
*alegre, alegramente*: *Mi profesor enseña biología alegramente.*

175. Mi abuela cocina maravillosamente. Cocina maravillosamente mi abuela.
Me gusta mucho jugar en la computadora.
La profesora está siempre ocupada.
Caminas muy lentamente.
Estoy un poco cansada hoy. Hoy estoy un poco cansada.

176. Answers will vary but might include: *Yo miro la televisión de vez en cuando. Julia nunca mira la televisión. Andrés mira la televisión con mucha frecuencia.*

177. Answers will vary but might include: *abajo*, *acá*, *adelante*, *adentro*, *aquí*, *allá*, *arriba*, *debajo*, *delante*, *detrás*, *encima*, *lejos*.

178.

| a | n | o | c | h | e | y | ñ | u | p | i | h | l | k | a | h |
|---|---|---|---|---|---|---|---|---|---|---|---|---|---|---|---|
| p | d | é | o | d | e | s | p | u | é | s | d | m | i | o | o |
| a | v | a | d | r | f | s | i | l | w | d | p | é | h | d | y |
| s | w | b | t | e | m | p | r | a | n | o | i | p | a | j | é |
| m | a | ñ | a | n | a | r | l | n | e | n | r | m | b | p | í |

179. -er: ía, ías, ía, íamos, ían
-ar: aba, abas, aba, ábamos, aban
-ir: ía, ías, ía, íamos, ían

180. ir, ser, ver. A possible mnemonic device is VIS a vis.